2001

ATLAS:1

Atlas would like to thank Litho-Tech Colour Printers for their invaluable support, skill and commitment to the highest possible standards of photographic reproduction in the printing of this, our first issue.

Much has changed since Litho-Tech was founded, but the idea of ink on paper has, thankfully, remained in place. Advances in technology have dispensed with many of the traditional skills involved with printing. Twenty five years ago it would have taken approximately one hundred and sixty hours to produce the plates required for this book. Today, using a computer-to-plate system, they can be completed in under ten hours and at twice the screen ruling.

Initially, a series of tests were undertaken in collaboration with Trebruk, the paper manufacturers, to assess the most suitable techniques for pre-press and printing. With so many variations in colour balance across the range of images it was decided that a four colour process was the most practical method of reproduction. There were two problems to resolve, firstly to compensate for the fact that although the paper is clean white, many of the prints are variously toned. Secondly some of the collections, such as Curtis, have extreme hues within the image detail. The solution was to individually adjust the bias of the cyan, magenta and yellow channels to match the intricacies of the originals. However, the images which have a more neutral colour balance would appear too warm if this technique was used, so for these a process called UCR (Under Colour Removal) was applied. UCR involves maintaining a full strength black while using the remaining three process colours to underpin it and provide a boost. This allows the adjustment of each colour without overly affecting the density of the black.

In the future it is doubtless that advances in technology will force higher levels of automation and quality management and a lesser requirement for traditional skills. With this the quality advantage enjoyed by companies such as Litho-Tech will start to diminish. Derek Adnitt, Sales and Marketing Director of Litho-Tech: "We see our future success being able to offer the very highest levels of customer service. Our internal training process ensures that the knowledge of traditional skills remains a standard, and we have developed a free customer training programme. Quality Management is central to all working procedures and commands a full time role. Litho-Tech is accredited to ISO 9002 (Quality Management) and ISO 14001 (Enviromental Management)."

We are delighted that Litho-Tech have decided to mark their 25th birthday by the printing of this first issue of Atlas.

CONTENTS

FINE ART PHOTOGRAPHY

FROM THE WORLD'S GREAT PHOTOGRAPHIC ARCHIVES

WELCOME TO THIS, THE FIRST ATLAS BOOK OF FINE ART ARCHIVAL PHOTOGRAPHY OFFERED FOR SALE FROM THE WORLD'S LEADING PHOTOGRAPHIC ARCHIVES.

Atlas exists to promote the work of pioneering nineteenth and early twentieth century photographers, and the cream of contemporary fine art photographic imagery through high quality modern limited edition prints. The collections represented span the world, from the masterpieces of twentieth century photographers such as Paul Strand, Alfred Stieglitz, Edward Steichen and Edward Weston to Edward S. Curtis's famous photographs of North American native Indians to the classic images of China and its peoples by John Thomson; from early photographs of Tibet to Alan Villiers' stunning maritime photographs of the twenties and the world-renowned images by Frank Hurley of Sir Ernest Shackleton's Endurance Expedition to the Antarctic.

All prints are made using original negatives from major archives around the globe and are hand-printed and finished to the most exacting standards on the finest quality fibre-based paper and are retouched and toned to ensure maximum longevity. In every case, contracts exist to protect all Atlas editions in perpetuity. As such, quantities are limited, and Atlas early boxed set Collectors' Editions have already soared in value. For those of more modest means, or who simply wish to obtain faithful renditions of important historic photographs, an excellent selection of single prints is available from less than £200.

The Atlas Gallery stages from four to five exhibitions per year, most exhibitions being accompanied by a lavishly illustrated catalogue. Potential buyers are recommended to visit The Atlas Gallery premises in central London, or to view these exhibition catalogues which are available for each of the collections represented.

Atlas is published twice a year. Annual subscription includes the two issues of this, the Atlas Book and also brings with it invitations to all opening nights and copies of all individual exhibition catalogues published during the year, which will be mailed to you free and special offers on individual works or portfolios. Membership of Atlas will place you amongst the most discerning buyers of photographic art world-wide.

Clearly, there is no better time to start or to expand your own collection of important photographic images. But act quickly to secure your choice, bearing in mind that prices are subject to change without notice as supplies diminish. Photographs from Atlas collections represent a unique opportunity to acquire rare photographic treasures at affordable prices. Contained within are only a selection from a vast array of superb photographic work for sale.

To order photographic prints or catalogues, or to subscribe to Atlas for the coming year and also receive free of charge all exhibition catalogues for the next twelve months, or to find out more about other special offers for subscribers, please complete the order form enclosed on page 67.

Opposite page: Young Boy, Gondeville, Charente, France, 1951. © 1971, Aperture Foundation Inc., Paul Strand Archive

THE APERTURE COLLECTION

ALONG SIDE THE CLASSIC BUT MORE HISTORICAL IMAGERY FROM MANY OF THE ARCHIVES REPRESENTED IN THIS FIRST ISSUE OF ATLAS, WE ARE DELIGHTED TO PRESENT A SELECTION OF SUPERB LIMITED EDITION PRINTS FROM THE APERTURE FOUNDATION FOR PHOTOGRAPHY AND THE VISUAL ARTS. THESE PRINTS ARE THE WORK OF PHOTOGRAPHIC ARTISTS, WHOSE REPUTATIONS ARE WORLD-RENOWNED. PHOTOGRAPHERS SUCH AS PAUL STRAND, ALFRED STIEGLITZ AND EDWARD STEICHEN WHO EXPLORED WHAT WAS TO BE KNOWN AS THE AESTHETIC OF "PURE" PHOTOGRAPHY ARE TODAY REGARDED AS AMONGST THE MOST IMPORTANT PHOTOGRAPHERS IN THE HISTORY OF THE ART FORM.

Founded in New York in 1952, the Aperture Foundation is committed to promoting the ideal of photography as one of the most powerful forms of human expression and communication. Over the course of the ensuing years, the Foundation has established a high calibre reputation in the spheres of both historic and contemporary photography.

One of its cornerstones is the Paul Strand Archive, which was donated in 1983 and comprises all the works of Paul Strand - negatives, prints, letters, writings, library and memorabilia. The same Archive, jointly located in Lakeville, Connecticut, and Millerton, New York, also includes photographs by Ansel Adams, Robert Adams, Bill Brandt, Harry Callahan, Robert Frank, Danny Lyon, Aaron Siskind, Jerry Uelsmann, Edward Weston and Minor White. Publishing and exhibition ventures are prominent amongst Aperture's activities. The Foundation has published 155 editions of its quarterly journal together with more than 300 books - the latter including both monographs on individual photographers and general discussions about the history and nature of photography. Exhibitions have been undertaken in association with the International Centre for Photography and the Smithsonian in the USA, and the Victoria and Albert Museum and the Arts Council in the UK. Aperture also maintains the Burden Gallery, which is located in its New York City headquarters.

Through its established and much respected limited edition print and portfolio programme, Aperture has fostered interest in the work of both well-known and lesser-known photographers. A collection that combines both is the *Golden Age of British Photography* portfolio, which presents sixteen hand-pulled

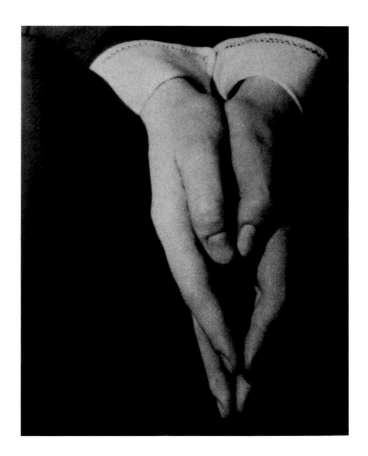

photogravures of rare masterpieces from some of the most important historic photographers, including; William Henry Fox Talbot, Henry Peach Robinson, Lady Clementina Hawarden, Frederick H. Evans and Julia Margaret Cameron. Wherever possible, the plates have been made using the photographers' original negatives, all rendered under the close supervision of the Keeper of the Victoria and Albert Museum Collection in order to ensure maximum fidelity. Each image is printed on 100% cotton-rag paper using inks created especially for the project. Image sizes vary, but all are printed on a uniform 20x16 inch paper sheet size.

Dominating the Aperture Collection are many works by Paul Strand, including portfolios created in association with Richard Benson during 1975 and 1976. Strand himself made few prints of even his most famous images, but supervised, approved and in some cases even signed these special sets. Those that are not signed by Strand in person have been signed by his wife Hazel on his behalf, and bear the authorising seal of the Paul Strand Foundation.

Other images within the Aperture Archive, as well as collections of images by Steichen and Stieglitz, include Edward Weston's famous 'Nude Floating', Annie Leibovitz's portrait of Merce Cunningham, Robert Capa's 'Pablo Picasso and Francois Gilot, Golfe-Juan, France, August 1948' and Philip Jones Griffiths's 'Street Scene, South Korea, 1967'.

PHOTOGRAPHS FROM

THE ROYAL GEOGRAPHICAL SOCIETY AND PHOTOGRAPHY SHARE A HISTORY. THE SOCIETY WAS FOUNDED IN 1830, PHOTOGRAPHY WAS INVENTED AND "FIXED" DURING THE 1830S. BUT NOT ONLY DO THEY SHARE A HISTORY, BOTH DISCIPLINES SHARE A NINETEENTH CENTURY BELIEF IN THE OBJECTIVITY OF SCIENCE. GEOGRAPHY AND PHOTOGRAPHY WERE BOTH PART OF THE NEW SCIENCES THAT ALLOWED THE VICTORIANS TO DOCUMENT AND STUDY THE WORLD AROUND THEM WITH EMPIRICAL AUTHORITY. MANY EARLY FELLOWS OF THE SOCIETY WERE ALSO IMPORTANT CONTRIBUTORS TO THE DEVELOPMENT OF PHOTOGRAPHY, MEN LIKE SIR JOHN HERSCHEL, INVENTOR OF THE CYANOTYPE PROCESS AND FRANCIS GALTON, INSTIGATOR OF THE COMPOSITE PHOTOGRAPH.

From the date the Society was founded it has sought to collect books and maps and, as the Royal Charter states "advance geographical science and improve geographical knowledge". Once photography was established as an empirical recording device, the Society began to actively encourage its use by members and to collect the photograph in all its forms. In the Geographical Journal, from the 1880s onwards, a note was included asking Fellows to forward copies of the photographs they took on their travels to the Map Curator of the Society. Thus the photographic collection began, and its form ranged from original prints, negatives or lantern-slides. Today, some 170 years after its foundation, the Society estimates that the photographic holdings number over a half a million objects. A unique attribute of the collection is that much of the material has been donated and that many of the donors have been the actual photographers, even if they saw themselves as primarily travellers, explorers, surveyors, geographers or government officials. The camera was an instrument by which to faithfully record and document their experiences of the world, its people and its landscapes.

It was Sir Clements Markham's belief in Captain R. F. Scott which eventually led him to assume leadership of the National Antarctic Expedition 1901-1904 in the ship "Discovery" which was specially built in Dundee for scientific research. The "Discovery" was designed to be strong, which was fortunate as the winter months of 1902 and 1903 proved to be exceptionally cold and the ship was soon frozen into the ice from which she eventually had to be blasted free in 1904. The Society was instrumental in this pioneering expedition and today holds the original glass plate negatives taken during the three years that Scott and his men were away gathering valuable scientific information about this "terra incognita". The expedition also set out to map as much of the interior of Antarctica as possible and after a freezing three month journey Scott, with Ernest Shackleton and Dr E.A. Wilson reached the then "furthest south", at 82° 17'S. One of the photographs in the collection shows the three determined men before they set off for their long journey. They are dressed

in their protective clothing against the biting cold, which Scott later wrote they never got used to, but just learned how to cope with. Behind them sits a heavily loaded sledge bedecked with flags. These flags were individually designed and inscribed by Markham for each senior officer aboard Discovery with personal motto's. Scott's read "Ready, aye Ready".

Scott and Shackleton are considered to be two of the greatest British polar explorer's of all time and the Society is pleased to have had associations with both men. Another image in the collection shows a portrait of Sir Ernest Shackleton, on board the ship *Quest* 1921-1922, his final expedition. He was known simply to his men as the Boss.

The earliest image in the Society's photographic collection was taken in Zanzibar and is just a tiny part of the Society's holdings on Africa. The Society's links with Speke, Burton and Livingstone are well known, but in this collection, we focus on the work of Sir Harry Johnston. Johnston was a dynamic man who saw himself as an anthropologist, geographer, diplomat and artist. His use of the camera was prolific and today the Society houses over a thousand glass plate negatives taken by him during his career in East Africa and the Caribbean. Johnston had an extensive knowledge of the African territories and people and was the first to write and translate a dictionary of the Bantu languages. It was with this knowledge that he negotiated a number of treaties on behalf of the Colonial Office. One striking image shows the young Kabaka of Uganda. Because of his work in Africa, Johnston was invited by President Theodore Roosevelt to discuss the latter's forthcoming expedition to Africa. Roosevelt also wanted Johnston's opinion on the New World's African Diaspora's community. In 1908-1909 Johnston journeyed through the Southern States of America and the Caribbean thoroughly researching the area's history, environment and society and recorded his journey in photographs. His images capture people in their everyday surroundings; they show the hustle and bustle of everyday life and are a unique historical record of Caribbean life. Today some of Johnston's views

THE ROYAL GEOGRAPHICAL SOCIETY

may not sit comfortably, but what is interesting is that he believed that the Diaspora community could, and should, be able to rule itself, thus alienating himself and his work from prevalent colonial views. In a number of photographs the subject looks at the photographer in a confrontational stance, defying both Johnston and us as viewers and re-defining many stereo-types that we might have.

The images in the collection come from all over the world and in it we have tried to give you a taste of the diversity. From Everard Im Thurn's view in British Guiana in 1878, from an original wet plate collodion negative to Sir J. B. Thurston's images of the Solomon Islands in the South Pacific, the range of material in the collection allows us a glimpse of how these geographers and photographers viewed the world.

The Society also holds important collections from Asia. From the mountains to the plains this continent was exhaustively surveyed, mapped and photographed. One particular collection we are proud to hold is the work of Frank Kingdon-Ward, botanist, traveller and winner of the Society's Royal Medal. Kingdon-Ward specialised in the study and distribution of plants in Indo-China, particularly the rhododendrums, primulas and lilies. He located the rare Blue Poppy and brought back its seed to Kew, where it can still be seen today. His forays lead him to travel in remote regions relying on the hospitality of the local people he met. The pictures he took give us an understanding of the world he inhabited, and the dangers which he faced. "Cane Bridge" shows a local porter carrying a small puppy across a suspension bridge made of cane, Kingdon-Ward presents this event, not as a Romantic vision, but as part of his everyday existence.

"Everest" is a word of mythic proportions and it inspires the imagination. The Society has had a long association with the world's highest mountain, named after the Surveyor General of India, Sir George Everest. The Society, with the Alpine Club, has supported numerous expeditions to climb Everest particularly during the 1920s, 1930s and the successful ascent in 1953 by

Tenzing Norgay and Edmund Hillary. An important photograph in the collection is of "Everest from a Camp at 20,000 feet" and was taken by A.F.R. Wollaston on the first official Mount Everest expedition of 1921. It shows Everest, majestic in the background with a small inconsequential camp in the foreground. Lt Col. Howard-Bury writes about how he and the other members sat and watched the extraordinary sight of Everest from this camp for some time, transfixed by the mountain and the "plume of smoke" the wind creates at the summit.

Photography was an important element of the expedition. Major Wheeler carried out a photographic survey of the terrain and the team members had various cameras with which to record their accomplishments. The camera with which this image was taken was a Hare Camera, leant to the expedition and in fact for a short time attained the record of reaching the greatest height for so large a camera, at 22,500 feet. The members all had various problems with the photographic equipment they took. Mallory famously put the negative plates back to front, and Howard-Bury was "gassed" by fumes from the fixing agent that he used, to such an extent that he lost his voice for several days. These early images of Everest taken as a scientific record are quite astonishing in their ability to transport the viewer to another time and place. It is the significant detail in the image that captures the imagination, the lone chair set out at a short distance from the camp at 20,000 feet allows the viewer to escape into the image, and to take the seat themselves. Photographs are only fragments of life, but they are significant details, which allow us, the viewer, a space in which to connect with and locate events, places and people. It is interesting to think of the early geographers and photographers using the science of photography to record their world. Would they have had any idea that future generations would want to use these images, to as John Berger writes, "refer to that which historical time has no right to destroy."

Joanna Scadden - Royal Geographical Society Picture Library Manager

FROM THE DARK

A METICULOUS APPROACH ENSURES THAT ALL ATLAS COLLECTIONS ARE PRINTED AS FAITHFULLY AS POSSIBLE, BUT BECAUSE NEGATIVES DETERIORATE WITH AGE, TO RE-CREATE THIS CAN BE CHALLENGING. EVERY NEGATIVE HAS TO BE MATCHED TO THE RIGHT PAPER AND WITH THE INCREASING SCARCITY OF HIGH QUALITY FIBRE-BASED PAPER, PARTICULARLY GRADED PAPERS, AND PAPERS SUITED TO THE REPRODUCTION OF EARLY PHOTOGRAPHIC IMAGERY, THIS IS A JOB IN WHICH WE INVEST A CONSIDERABLE AMOUNT OF TIME. THE 2000 SQUARE FEET OF DARK ROOMS WHERE ALL ATLAS COLLECTIONS, WITH THE EXCEPTION OF THE APERTURE COLLECTIONS, ARE PRODUCED ARE SITUATED IN THE SAME BUILDING AS THE ATLAS GALLERY AND HAVE BEEN DESIGNED AND EQUIPPED WITH THE REQUIREMENTS OF ARCHIVE PRINTING SPECIFICALLY IN MIND.

Enshrined in all our collections is a deep respect for the work of the original artists. It is this dedication which is central to the work of re-creating the photographs of photographers such as Edward Curtis whose own passion for their subjects was so intense. In Curtis's case it was his life's work to record the faces of a race of people who were soon to almost dissappear and through these images to tell the story of their culture and history. The passion involved in the process of creating an image must thus be held in high respect and matched in the process of interpreting the negative years later. Each of the Atlas collections thus demands a completely different approach. In some cases, for instance, changes in technology mean that enlargements can be made of work which at the time photographs were taken was not possible, the technology of enlarging from negatives being a late nineteenth century development. However, in all the work of Atlas as publisher and Melvin Cambettie Davis as printer, the intention is, as much as possible, to recreate the intentions and atmosphere envisioned by the original photographer. This also reflects one the key aspects of collecting fine art photography, for in collecting photography one is, in a way, collecting history itself.

ROOM

PHOTOGRAPHS FROM THE ROYAL GEOGRAPHICAL SOCIETY

The Royal Geographical Society Portfolio 1 comprises 30 stunning images, each one limited to 300 copies. All prints are on 16x20 inch paper; image size varies. The prints are individually numbered by hand, and each is sold with a certificate of authenticity, frame caption and presentation envelope. Additionally, the first 25 sets are available as a Deluxe Collector's Edition comprising all 30 images in a finely-crafted presentation clamshell case. All prints are published on an exclusive basis in collaboration with the Royal Geographical Society, which retains copyright. All images © copyright The Royal Geographical Society. Reproduction is strictly prohibited.

To order a full illustrated catalogue of this collection, turn to the Catalogue Order Form on page 67.

PORTFOLIO 1

14

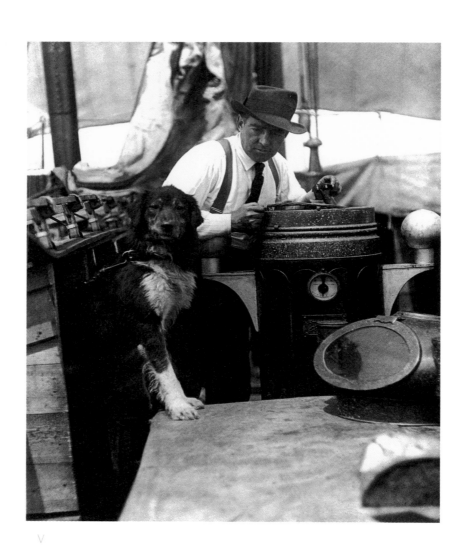

V

THE SHADOW CATCHER.
PHOTOGRAPHS OF NORTH AMERICAN INDIANS BY EDWARD S. CURTIS

Edward Sheriff Curtis (1868-1952) is recognised as the most important photographer of the Native Indian People of his time. His photographic record of every tribe of North American Indians was originally planned as a five-year project, but went on to occupy him until death. His final body of work numbered more than 400,000 pictures, making Curtis's work the most important visual record of any single native people anywhere in the world. The pictures were collated and set down for all time in a monumental 20-volume work entitled *The North American Indian*, which was published between 1907 and 1930, and was limited to 272 sets.

The 1960s and 1970s saw a huge revival of interest in the work of Edward Curtis, and his pictures of North American Indians have become some of the most sought-after and collected prints of modern times. Atlas Limited Editions has now reprinted a limited edition of 50 silver gelatin prints. Among the set are some of Curtis's most famous pictures, together with others that are little known - and some that were never issued as part of the *The North American Indian*. To create these images, copy negatives were made of original archive vintage prints held at the Library of Congress, Washington DC, and these were then hand-printed and sepia toned by master printer Melvin Cambettie Davies, at Master Mono, London on Kodak Ektalure - the finest monochrome paper in the world today.

Each print is on 16x20 inch paper, with the image area to match, as closely as possible, the vintage prints held in the collection of the Prints and Photographs Division at the Library of Congress. In further keeping with Curtis's original photogravure prints, the contemporary images are strictly limited to an edition of 272 copies. Prints are individually numbered by hand and are sold with a certificate of authenticity and limitation, and are enclosed in custom-made presentation envelopes. In addition, the first 25 sets are available as a special Collector's Edition of all 50 images in a classic presentation library clamshell case.

To order a full illustrated catalogue of this collection, turn to the Catalogue Order Form on page 67.

PORTFOLIO 2

Atlas is delighted to be able to offer the full choice of all Aperture's important limited edition prints for sale and are exclusive agents for all Aperture prints in the UK and Europe. The images shown on the following pages are only a small selection of these historic images. Editions, image types and paper sizes vary.
Copyright: I © 1976, Aperture Foundation Inc., Paul Strand Archive. II Courtesy of The Aperture Foundation. III © 1971, Aperture Foundation

Inc., Paul Strand Archive. IV © 1955, Aperture Foundation Inc., Paul Strand Archive. V © 1981, Aperture Foundation Inc., Paul Strand Archive. VI © 1977, Aperture Foundation Inc., Paul Strand Archive. VII Courtesy of The Aperture Foundation.

To order a full price list for all the prints available from these collections, turn to the Catalogue Order Form on page 67.

PORTFOLIO 3

IV

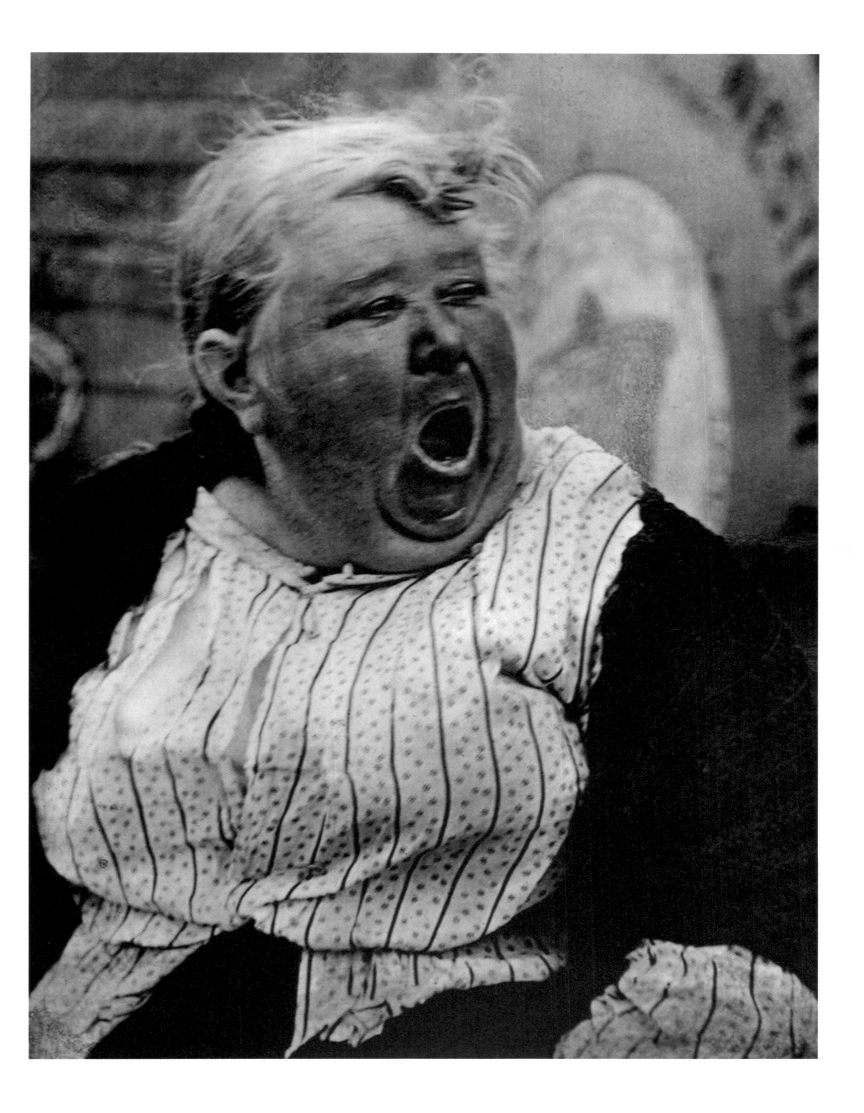

THE HURLEY COLLECTION
PHOTOGRAPHS BY FRANK HURLEY OF SIR ERNEST SHACKLETON'S
TRANS-ANTARCTIC EXPEDITION, 1914-17

The now famous Australian photographer Frank Hurley first travelled to the Antarctic in 1911 with Sir Douglas Mawson, after bribing a railway guard to get a seat next to him in a train carriage in order to effect an introduction. It was similar resourcefulness, four years later, that prevented Hurley's photographs of Sir Ernest Shackleton's Trans-Antarctic expedition from sinking to the sea-bed when their ship, the Endurance, fixed solid in the ice, was crushed by the Spring thaw. Hurley dived into the freezing water and rescued 500 glass plates - only to be told by Shackleton that he would have to discard most on account of the arduous journey that now lay ahead. Around 120 plates were retained: the rest Hurley smashed on the ice.

Shackleton, Hurley and the rest of the crew of the Endurance dragged three of the ship's lifeboats across the ice to open water, then rowed to Elephant Island off the northern end of the Antarctic Peninsula. At this point, Shackleton left with five crew in one of the lifeboats, modified for sailing, to reach South Georgia. The journey was of 800 miles across treacherous waters, and was followed by a difficult climb over South Georgia's mountain range. When Shackleton and his party finally reached the whaling station of Stromness Bay, they immediately set about mounting a rescue for the remaining men - all of whom were eventually brought to safety without the loss of a single life. The story of the survival of Hurley's negatives is thus almost as astonishing as the story of the survival of the expedition itself. These historic early images of Antarctica both tell the amazing story of this famous epic of endurance and depict the acute beauty and splendour of the Antarctic landscape itself. After the return of the expedition Hurley's negatives were presented to The Royal Geographical Society, who retain ownership and copyright. The prints in this now widely known edition of his photographs have been made using these historic glass plates.

Publication of The Hurley Collection in 1995 marked the first time that these photographs had been issued as a limited edition series. The intervening five years have seen an enormous explosion of interest in Hurley as a photographer and a consequently steep rise in demand for vintage prints. The prints in this collection thus represent an unique opportunity to acquire, at an affordable price, one of these historic images.

The set comprises 35 stunning images, each one limited to 400 copies. All prints are on 16x20 inch paper, with approximately 12x16 inch picture areas. The prints are individually numbered by hand, and each is sold with a certificate of authenticity and presentation envelope. Additionally, the first 25 sets are available as a Deluxe Collector's Edition comprising all 35 images in a finely-crafted presentation clamshell case. The prints are published on an exclusive basis in collaboration with the Royal Geographical Society, which retains copyright: reproduction is strictly prohibited. All images © The Royal Geographical Society.

To order a full illustrated catalogue of this collection, turn to the Catalogue Order Form on page 67.

PORTFOLIO 4

35

III

THE JOHN THOMSON COLLECTION - FINE PHOTOGRAPHS OF CHINA AND THE FAR EAST

John Thomson's birth coincided with that of the photographic medium itself, falling almost midway between the publication of William Henry Fox Talbot's landmark book *The Pencil of Light* in 1834, and Fox Talbot's subsequent announcement of the negative process in February 1839. Thomson was captivated by photography from an early age, and in 1862 embarked on his first journey to the Far East. Initially, he established a studio in Penang, but quickly he decided that more interesting pictures could be taken in the field - quite literally, in some cases.

Thomson's subjects reflected the full gamut of human existence, from street traders to noblemen, and gamblers to court officials. In Siam, where he arrived in 1865, Thomson was granted an audience with King Mongkut, and was given permission to photograph in full the city, its ceremonies and its people. From Siam, Thomson then travelled to Cambodia, where he took the first ever photographs of the country's ancient capital, Angkor Thom. After a sojourn in his native Edinburgh, Thomson set off again to the Far East in 1867 - this time with the deliberate intention systematically to compile a complete photographic record of the peoples of China. This project took four years to complete and involved travelling in excess of 4000 miles. It portrayed not only the inhabitants of Hong Kong and mainland China, but also the temples, tombs, rivers and monuments of the land. Together, his images were compiled into a magnificent four-volume set entitled *Illustrations of China and its People* - without doubt the most important nineteenth photographic century work of its type.

After his return to England, Thomson began his second great photographic project, a photo-documentation of the lives of the urban under-classes and slum-dwellers who lived on the streets of London in the late 1870s and early 1880s. After his death, all of Thomson's negatives were sold to pharmaceuticals magnate Henry Wellcome: today, the collection belongs to The Wellcome Trust, which has given consent for these limited edition prints to be produced from Thomson's original negatives.

All prints are 16x20 inches on Kodak Ektalure fibre-base paper. The edition comprises 40 of the most striking images taken by Thomson of China and the Far East, each limited to 350 copies. The prints are individually numbered by hand, and each is sold with a special limitation certificate, frame caption and presentation envelope. In addition, the first 20 sets are available as a special Collector's Edition of all 40 images in a hand-crafted clamshell case. All images © The Wellcome Institute.

To order a full illustrated catalogue of this collection, turn to the Catalogue Order Form on page 67.

PORTFOLIO 5

THE ALAN VILLIERS COLLECTION.
THE LAST OF THE WIND SHIPS. PHOTOGRAPHS BY ALAN VILLIERS, 1928-1933

Alan John Villiers (1903-1982) was captivated by "tall ships" or ocean-going cargo vessels at an early age in Australia, where he was born and brought up. He subsequently sailed to England, and during the course of his life progressed up to the rank of Commander RNVR. He participated in the Normandy Landings of World War Two, and was awarded the Distinguished Service Cross for his efforts. But it was an earlier time that provided the pictures in this collection - a time when the last of the tall ships sailed the seas.

Never before have the photographs of Alan Villiers been available for sale as a limited edition series. The 33 pictures selected here are taken from the collection of the National Maritime Museum in London, which Villiers helped to found, and cover his years on the *Herzogin Cecilie* (1928), the *Grace Harwar* (1929) and the *Parma* (1932-33). As such, these images represent some of the finest images from the last days of merchant sailing ships, and are arguably the most important photo-historical records of this period of maritime history.

To prepare these prints, Atlas Limited Editions gained access to the original negatives, from which have been created new printing negatives that will afterwards become the property of the National Maritime Museum - so helping to preserve the work of Alan Villiers for years to come. All prints are silver gelatin prints, archivally printed on 16x20 inch Ilford semi-matt fibre paper by Melvin Cambettie Davies at Master Mono in London.

Each image is strictly limited to 350 copies. The image area is approximately 13x17 inches, with some variation due to different negative formats. Prints are individually numbered by hand and are sold with a certificate of authenticity and limitation, and are enclosed in custom-made presentation envelopes. In addition, the first 25 sets are available as a Deluxe Collector's Edition of all 33 images in a hand-crafted presentation clamshell case. All prints are published on an exclusive basis in collaboration with the National Maritime Museum, which retains copyright. All images © The National Maritime Museum

To order a full illustrated catalogue of this collection, turn to the Catalogue Order Form on page 67.

PORTFOLIO 6

A CAMERA IN TIBET
THE PHOTOGRAPHS OF CHARLES BELL AND FREDERICK SPENCER CHAPMAN

Until the 13th Dalai Lama asked Charles Bell to take his portrait, Tibetan tradition had forbade depictions of reincarnate monks. Neither was this to be a single event, for the British Government's representative in Lhasa, who with Frederick Spencer Chapman was one of the first two Europeans to enter Lhasa by invitation, went on to photograph the Dalai Lama throughout his life. By this association, Bell was also permitted to photograph other strata of Tibetan life, and so was able to compile one of the first and most extensive visual archives of the country and its people in the early years of the twentieth century.

For his part, Spencer Chapman, who also had access to the uppermost echelons of Tibetan society, used both still and moving picture cameras to record the sights he was privileged to see. After just seven months in the country he had taken more than 2500 still pictures and recorded countless hours on 19,000 feet of moving film. In particular, he witnessed - and took colour photographs of - preparations for the annual New Year ceremonies. Significantly, the pictures do not show only dignitaries and monks, but also beggars and emaciated children. As such, they are a record of what actually was, rather than what is often imagined. Shortly afterwards, Tibet was annexed into the People's Republic of China - beginning a process that was to all but destroy Tibetan culture at home.

More than 700 of Bell's glass plate negatives survive to this day, 16 of which have been chosen for the Atlas edition. Spencer Chapman's colour photographs, of which only 75 survive, were recorded using Dufaycolour film - a positive (slide) material rather like today's transparency films. But whereas modern films are continuous, and can record any element of colour in any spot on the plate, Dufaycolour emulsions were discontinuous in that they were formed of separate red, green and blue-violet areas. The originals were intended to be viewed actual size, without enlargement, so that the 'screen' would not be visible. However, due to improved modern printing techniques, it has been possible to enlarge the prints in this edition to display Chapman's beautiful portraits and landscapes to greater effect. All the pictures are from the collection of the Pitt Rivers Museum at the University of Oxford. Charles Bell's negatives are printed on 16x20 inch silver gelatin paper, hand-crafted to the highest standard by master printer Melvin Cambettie Davies. Spencer Chapman's 9 Dufaycolours are printed using archival colour inks with an estimated longevity of at least 100 years by Michael Gray, curator of the Fox Talbot Museum, Lacock Abbey, Wiltshire. The edition consists of 25 images, each limited to 200 copies and numbered by hand and sold with a special limitation certificate, frame caption and presentation envelope. In addition, the first 20 sets are available as a special Collector's Edition of all 25 images presented in a hand-crafted clamshell case. All images © The Pitt Rivers Museum, University of Oxford.

To order a full illustrated catalogue of this collection, turn to the Catalogue Order Form on page 67.

PORTFOLIO 7

THE BEKEN COLLECTION
PHOTOGRAPHS OF OCEAN RACING YACHTS FROM
THE NINETEENTH AND EARLY TWENTIETH CENTURIES BY BEKEN OF COWES

The photographic firm of Beken was established by chemist and keen marine photographer Alfred Beken, who relocated from Canterbury to Cowes in 1888 - just seven years after the first photograph was taken there of a yacht underway. The Beken family improved on those first stumbling attempts with a number of innovations, principally those devised by Frank, Alfred's son.

Born in 1880, Frank adopted photography first as a hobby and then as a profession. He designed cameras specifically for yacht photography at sea, and became adept at portraying ocean racing vessels first from rowing boats moved into position in advance to capture race action, then from small launches running alongside. In view of his bobbing platform, Frank Beken used to trigger his pictures using a bulb release that he held in his mouth, as both hands were required to grip the camera. Focusing was by a scale that was marked not in distances but according to the size of vessel being photographed; dinghy, yacht or liner.

In turn, Frank's son Keith joined the Beken business in the 1930s, and continued the family tradition of designing and building bespoke cameras as well as in-house chemistries for processing the glass plates. Later, in the 1970s, Keith's own son Kenneth joined the firm. By that time, glass plates had given way to medium format roll-film, and dedicated cameras were replaced with Hasselblads, but the same devotion to the chosen subject remains to this day.

Thanks to its Cowes home, the Beken family has documented yachting as a sport almost since its inception; from the early days of wealthy patrons and majestic designs, through to the division between royal patronage by the likes of Queen Victoria and the Tsar of Russia versus yachting for all on a smaller scale. In 1914, Beken photographed one of the new 'submarine' vessels, and afterwards, between the wars, the family documented the growing democratisation of sailing as vessel sizes shrank and owner-skippers became the norm. In all, the collection is an outstanding testament to the British devotion to the sea and the lifestyle that went with those early racing passions.

In collaboration with Beken of Cowes, Atlas Limited Editions have produced a special series of 72 limited edition prints, drawn principally from the 75,000 glass plates that record vessels from the nineteenth and early twentieth centuries. Every image in the Atlas selection is hand-printed on 16x20 inch silver gelatin paper directly from the original negative, with an approximately 12x16 inch picture area. All are hand-toned, and each is limited to 250 copies. Prints are individually numbered, signed and titled by hand and are sold with a custom-made presentation envelope. All images © Beken of Cowes

To order a full illustrated catalogue of this collection, turn to the Catalogue Order Form on page 67.

PORTFOLIO 8

NEXT ISSUE

SUBSCRIBE NOW AND RECEIVE "THE SHADOW CATCHER" AND "THE JOHN THOMSON COLLECTION" CATALOGUES ABSOLUTELY FREE. NOT ONLY THAT: SUBSCRIBE NOW AND RECEIVE A SPECIAL £50 VOUCHER OFF YOUR FIRST PURCHASE FROM ANY OF THE ATLAS COLLECTIONS.

THE SECOND ISSUE OF ATLAS, DUE SEPTEMBER 2001 FEATURES DETAILS OF FIVE EXCITING NEW EXHIBITIONS AND COLLECTIONS IN 2001.

KARL BLOSSFELDT. PHOTOGRAVURES.

Taken from the first editions of Blossfeldt's famous works *Urformen der Kunst (Archetypes of Art)*, 1928 and *Wundergarten der Natur (Wondergarden of Nature)*, 1932. Blossfeldt's purpose in his famous photographs of flowers, plants and plant-life was initially to make photographs to inspire and act as reference material for textile designers, ironworkers and art students in the Germany of the 1920's and 1930's. However, his philosophy was soon to broaden to encompass the theory that all artistic form was derived from the natural world. This extensive exhibition marks the beginning of a continuous stock of Blossfeldt's work to be permanently on view at The Atlas Gallery. **Exhibition Dates: April 3rd - May 4th. Free catalogue to subscribers.**

SURFING SAN ONOFRE TO POINT DUME. 1936-1942.
PHOTOGRAPHS BY DON JAMES.

Limited edition platinum prints. We are delighted to bring to Great Britain this superb series of photographs showing the earliest days of surfing in California. The collection takes us back to a time when the earliest surfers were busy inventing the first American beach culture. The beautiful and nostalgic photographs that surfer Don James took of himself and his friends from 1936-46 capture the lost Eden of the California surf dream in all its glory and innocence. **Exhibition Dates: May 18th - July 31st. Accompanied by a beautiful 140 page illustrated book, reprinting over 100 photographs. (price £15 / £10 to subscribers)**

HERBERT PONTING. PHOTOGRAPHING THE WORLD.

An exhibition of vintage prints by Herbert Ponting covering India, Japan, Central Asia, Burma, China and the Antarctic, 1905 - 1920. Best known for his famous photographs of the Antarctic taken on Robert F. Scott's Terra Nova Expedition, Ponting's photographs of the rest of the world are rarely seen. This important exhibition focuses almost exclusively on these rare large-scale images from the gates of Peking to the ornamental flower gardens of Japan to pictures of rural life in Burma at the turn of the century. All prints are vintage photographer's prints, usually signed by Ponting or with his well-known blind-stamp. **Exhibition dates: September 12th - October 19th**

EDWARD STEICHEN.

Including portfolio and limited edition prints from The Aperture Foundation. The second of our exhibitions of work from Aperture focuses on the work of one of the great masters of early twentieth century photography. **Exhibition dates: October 26th - November 30th**

ATLAS CHRISTMAS EXHIBITION.

A special selection from all Atlas Collections. Exhibition dates: December 4th - January 31st 2002. Full details and reviews of all these new collections and exhibitions and much more in **THE NEXT ISSUE.** Please note exact exhibition dates may alter slightly. Subscribers will automatically receive a free catalogue for exhibitions where shown.

CES FOR PRINTS SHOWN IN THIS ISSUE OF ATLAS:

₃e 01:	£3,000
₃e 03:	£250
₃e 10:	£250
₃e 11:	£250
₃e 12:	£340
₃e 13:	£250
₃e 14:	£340
₃e 15:	£250
₃e 18:	£250
₃e 19:	£250
₃e 20:	£250
₃e 22:	£250
₃e 23:	£250
₃e 26:	£4,000
₃e 27:	£1,000
₃e 28:	POA
₃e 30:	£1,250
₃e 31:	£300
₃e 32:	£400
₃e 33:	£250
₃e 36:	£380
₃e 37:	£330
₃e 38:	£330
₃e 39:	£330
₃e 42:	£280
₃e 43:	£280
₃e 44:	£250
₃e 45:	£280
₃e 46:	£280
₃e 47:	£220
₃e 50:	£220
₃e 51:	£220
₃e 52:	£220
₃e 53:	£220
₃e 56:	£220
₃e 57:	£220
₃e 60:	£250
₃e 61:	£250
₃e 62:	£250
₃e 64:	£250
₃e 65:	£250

prices subject to VAT (17.5%)

ou would like another order form, please let us
₃w and we will send you one.

prints with the exception of The Aperture
llection are printed by Melvin Cambettie Davies at
ster Mono, London

as is published in Great Britain by Atlas Books
57 Tabernacle Street, London EC2A 4AA, England
: 020 7490 4540. www.atlasgallery.com

text © Atlas Books with the exception of:
otographs from the RGS. Portfolio 1 © RGS-IBG.

blished January 2001. Editorial Committee:
n Burdett, John Tarrent, Niki Michelin
3N 0-9539695-0-9
sign: Julia Bostock & Associates & Practical
eamers Design, (contact: via Atlas Gallery).
nted by: Litho-Tech Colour Printers, London.
per supplied by: Trebruk.

ORDER FORM

PLEASE DETACH AND SEND TO US AT THE ADDRESS SHOWN ON THE REVERSE.

CATALOGUES

	Price Per Catalogue inc. postage (Overseas price in brackets)	NO:	TOTAL:
The RGS. Portfolio 1	£5.00 (£6.00)		
The Shadow Catcher	£5.00 (£6.00)		
The Aperture Collection	Free		
The Hurley Collection	£5.00 (£6.00)		
The John Thomson Collection	£5.00 (£6.00)		
The Alan Villiers Collection	£5.00 (£6.00)		
A Camera In Tibet	£5.00 (£6.00)		
The Beken Collection	£3.00 (£4.00)		

SUBSCRIPTION

I would like to subscribe to Atlas,
please circle (Overseas price in brackets)

TOTAL:

PERIOD		
One Year	£80.00 (£90.00)	
Two Years	£150.00 (£170.00)	
Three Years	£200.00 (£220.00)	

ORDERS FOR PRINTS SHOWN IN THIS CATALOGUE:

PLEASE ADD £8.00 FOR POSTAGE (£20.00 OVERSEAS) PER PRINT

PAGE NUMBER	TITLE	QUANTITY	TOTAL
		TOTAL:	
	FOR ORDERS WITHIN THE EEC:	VAT: (17.5%)	
		TOTAL DUE:	

PAYMENT METHOD:

Cheque enclosed ☐   Please charge my credit card ☐   Total amount to be charged: ☐

Card number (VISA/MASTERCARD/AMEX)

☐☐☐☐ ☐☐☐☐ ☐☐☐☐ ☐☐☐☐ ☐☐☐☐

Expiry date: ☐☐ ☐☐   Signature: _____

Address: _____

Tel: _____   e-mail: _____

ATLAS: 55-57 Tabernacle Street. London EC2A 4AA

Tel: 020 7490 4540 Fax: 020 7490 4514

e-mail: order@atlasgallery.com www.atlasgallery.com